Fidget

Grows a
Pizza Garden...

by Jodie Fitz

Illustrated by Keira Curwen

Printed in the United States of America

Published 2017 by

Saratoga Springs Publishing LLC
Saratoga Springs, NY
SaratogaSpringsPublishing@gmail.com
www.SaratogaSpringsPublishing.com

Illustrations by Keira Curwen
Graphic Design by Alyssa Jackson

This book is based on a true story.

I have written it for my very own Little Miss Fidget
and her two big brothers.

. . . .

You all helped my imagination to soar
as I watched you grow and you have
filled my heart & soul with memories
that I will forever cherish.
Thank you!

It was summertime and Fidget's friend A.J.
was growing a garden.

Fidget thought it looked like a lot of fun.

"Mom, can we grow a garden?"
"Maybe. . . a garden is a lot of work," said mom.

"I'll think about it,"
answered mom.

The next morning mom had an idea.
"I was thinking, what would you say if
we grow a pizza garden?"

"I can't wait to tell A.J.!"

After lunch mom and Fidget
made a shopping list.

In the afternoon mom and Fidget went to the garden center to buy supplies for their pizza garden.

They filled their wagon with:

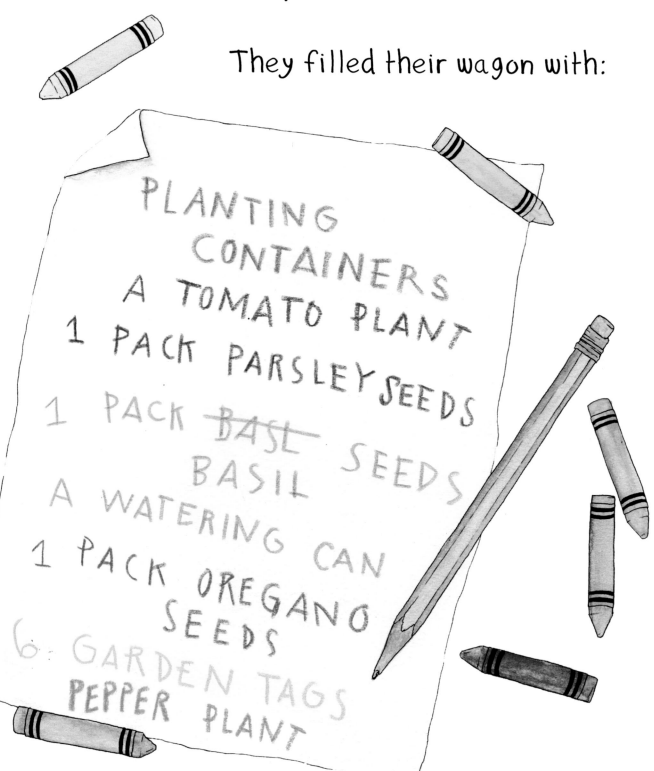

PLANTING CONTAINERS
A TOMATO PLANT
1 PACK PARSLEY SEEDS
1 PACK ~~BASL~~ BASIL SEEDS
A WATERING CAN
1 PACK OREGANO SEEDS
6 GARDEN TAGS
PEPPER PLANT

Mom and fidget each picked out their own pair of garden gloves and grabbed a bag of special dirt for vegetable growing.

When they got home they put on their garden gloves and filled the big planter half way with dirt.

Then they added the tomato plant and more dirt to cover the roots.

Fidget & Mom
filled the smaller
planters halfway
with dirt. Then they added
spice seeds to two of the planters
and the pepper plant to the other container.

When they were finished, they added
more dirt to cover the seeds and the roots.

Afterwards, they wrote the names
of each plant on garden tags
to add to the planters.

Next, it was time to water the plants!

Whoa

Hold on Fidget...

"Be careful not to over water the plants.
They need just the right amount of sun and
water. If you give them too much
they won't grow."

Mom and Fidget measured and drew lines on a big piece of paper to make a garden chart.

They filled in the days of the week
so that Fidget could keep track of
watering the plants.

When they were finished
they hung the chart
on the refrigerator.

Every day Fidget
watered the plants
and crossed off
the days.

Soon the plants began to grow.

Fidget was
so excited!

She imagined what her
pizza garden would look like.

Fidget woke up one morning and discovered
that the plants had mini green round circles
growing on them.

"We bought the wrong plants," complained Fidget.
"They're not growing pizza!"

"Sweetie, our plants don't grow pizza.
They grow the items we need to make the
pizza like tomatoes and spices for the sauce
and peppers for the top," explained mom.

"But I don't like tomatoes!" cried Fidget.

"But you like sauce," explained mom

"and sauce is made from tomatoes."

Fidget continued to water her garden
and before long the tomatoes had grown
bigger and had turned bright red.

One day fidget
plucked a tomato
and decided
to try it.

She discovered that she did like tomatoes.
They were sweet and delicious.

She grabbed another tomato on her way to swing.

She grabbed a couple of more tomatoes on her way to play with her chalk.

She grabbed another tomato to share with her dog Zoe.

The next day, Fidget went to water
the plants and realized
there weren't any more tomatoes...

"The tomatoes are gone!"

Fidget's mom had been watching her
eat the tomatoes as she was playing.

"It's okay. We will go to
the farmer's market and
buy some tomatoes,"
assured mom.

The next day, Mom and Fidget went
to the farmers market where
they bought more tomatoes.

When they got home
they put on their aprons
and rolled out some dough.

Then they cooked the tomatoes
and made the sauce.

When the sauce was finished
they layered their pizza,
topped it with the peppers
from their garden

and baked it in the oven.

When the pizza was finished baking,
Fidget and mom invited A.J. over
to eat pizza from their
pizza garden.

"This was fun,"
said A.J.

"I have an idea..."
said Fidget

"...let's grow an ice cream garden next!"

Visit www.jodiefitz.com/fidget for your free pizza garden chart & shopping list

Contact Jodie Fitz at jodie@jodiefitz.com for an author's visit.

Visit www.jodiefitz.com/fidget to learn how to make Taco Pizza, Monster pizzas & Grilled pizza

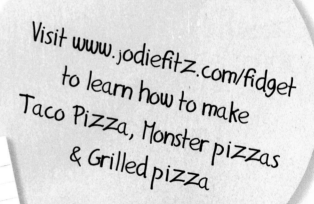

Join Fidget's email list at www.jodiefitz.com/fidget and receive more information about Fidget's adventures & more pizza growing tips & tricks.

ABout the Author:

Jodie Fitz is an author, speaker & creator of a Kids Cooking Club. She currently works in a six state area with a grocery retailer, traveling & cooking with children & families. She has worked with communities developing children's programming for over 10 years. As a wife & working mother of three, she has many stories to share, including those from her very own Little Miss Fidget. You can follow along with Jodie and learn all about her various programs, products and activities at www.jodiefitz.com

Get Social with Jodie.
Find her at JodieFitz
(instagram, twitter, google+)
or JodieFitzCooks (facebook & pinterest)

ABout the Illustrator:

Keira Curwen has been putting paint and pencil to paper for all of her years. Wearing both the hat of artist and an illustrator, her work ranges from paintings to greeting cards to printed editions. Originally from Galway, New York, she is currently making her home in Brooklyn while pursuing a BFA in Printmaking at Pratt Institute.

Made in the USA
San Bernardino, CA
26 March 2018